NORMAN SPITTAL

Jeremy Banx

The Many Deaths
of
Norman Spittal

Insect Publications

For
ANNE LASCELLES

Banx
PO Box 26455
London
SE10 9WY

www.jbanx.com

Copyright ©Jeremy Banx 1995

Designed by Rian "bedbug" Hughes

Printed in Guernsey by
THE GUERNSEY PRESS COMPANY
LIMITED

British Library Cataloguing in
publication data.
A catalogue record for this book is
available from the British Library.

ISBN 1 899781 005

975312468

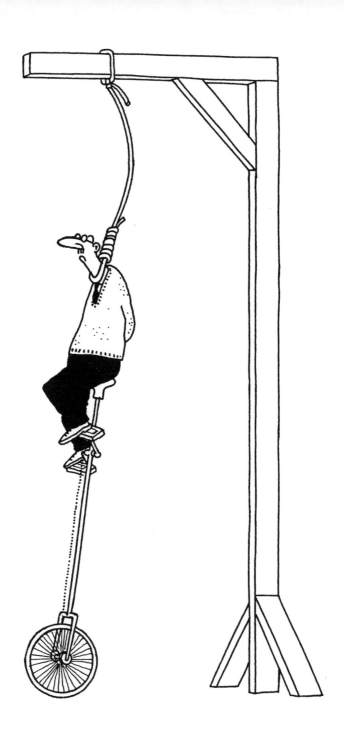

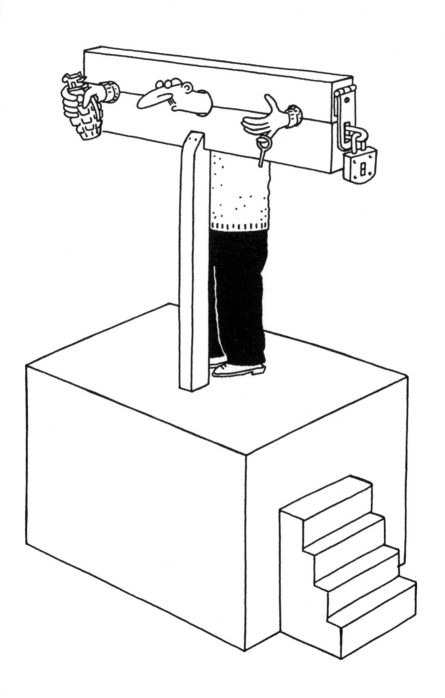

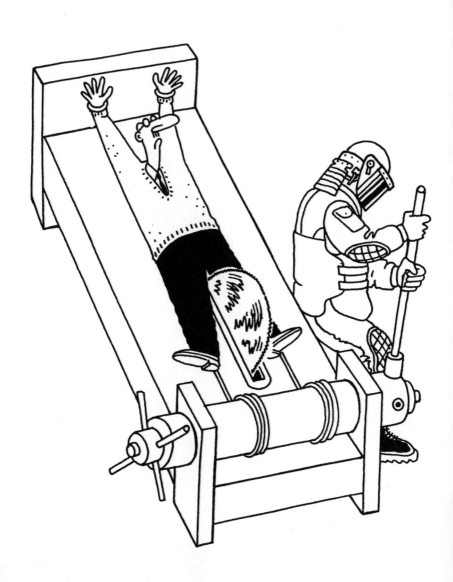

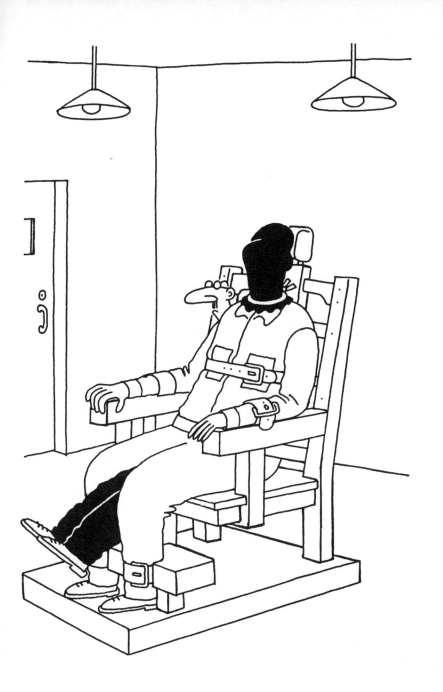

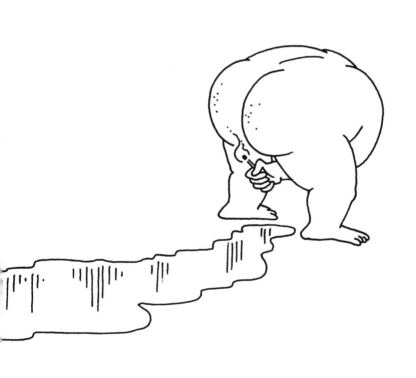

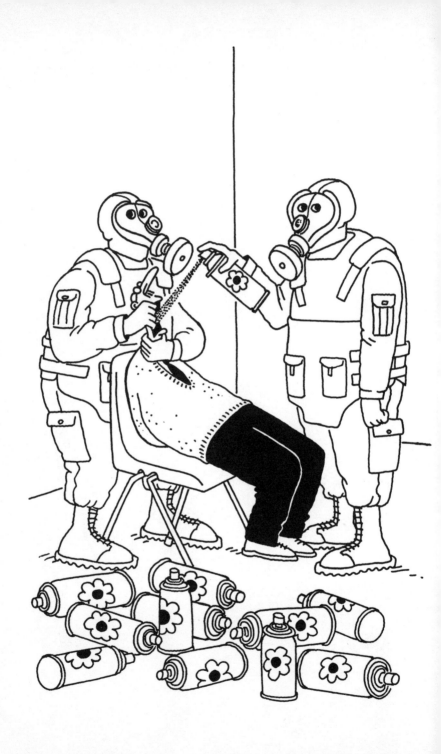

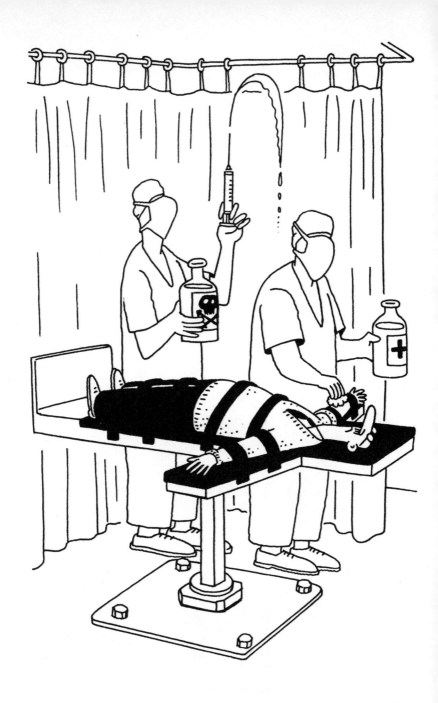

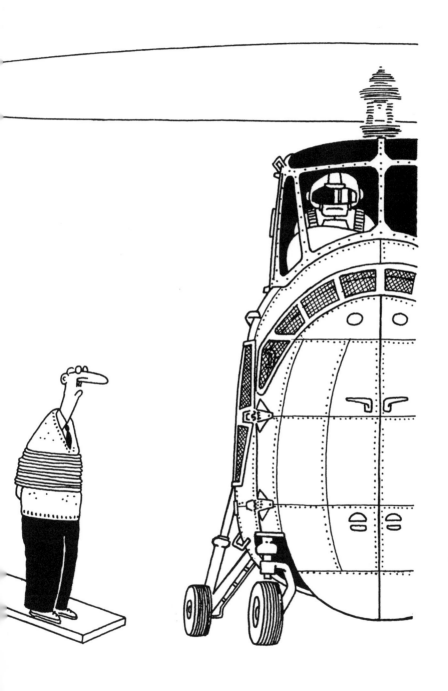

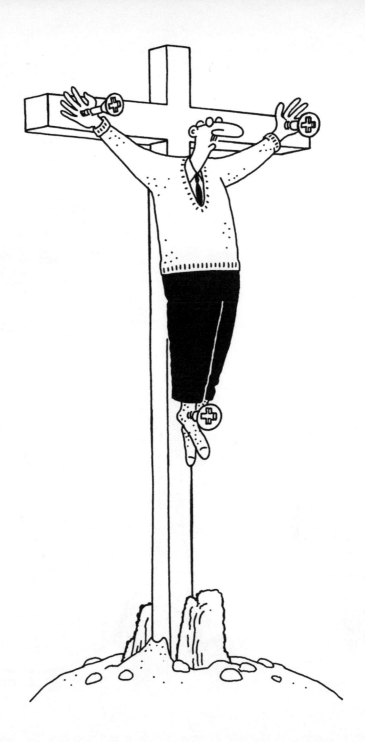

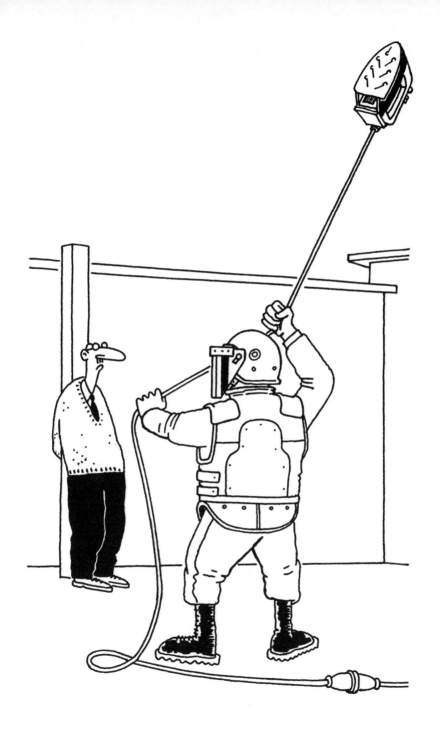

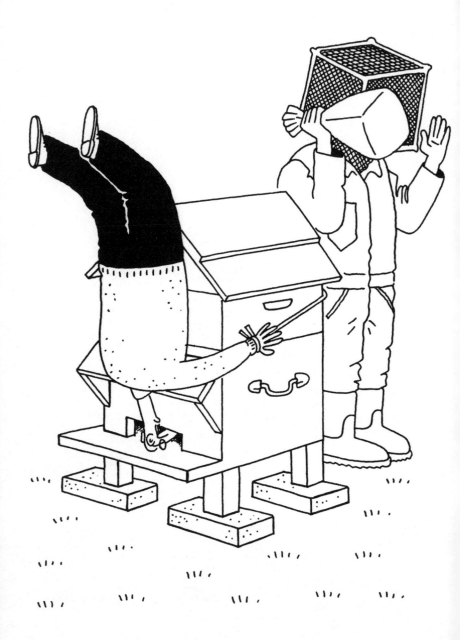

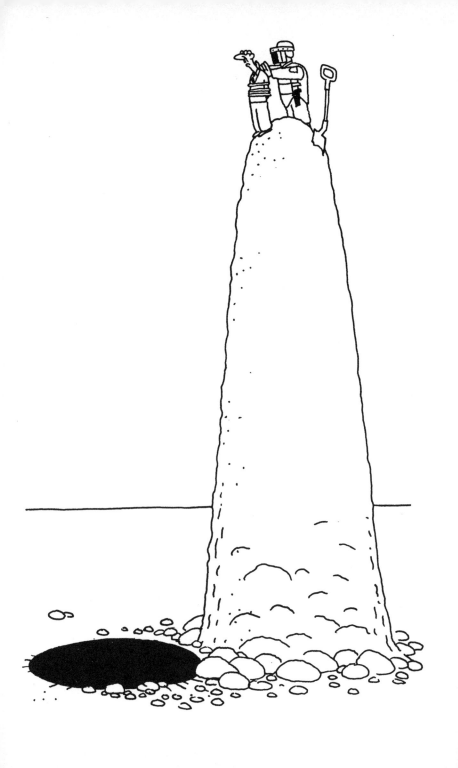

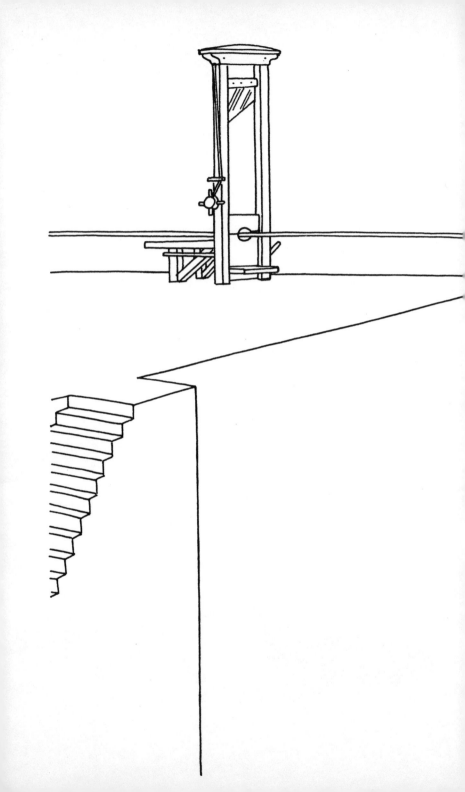

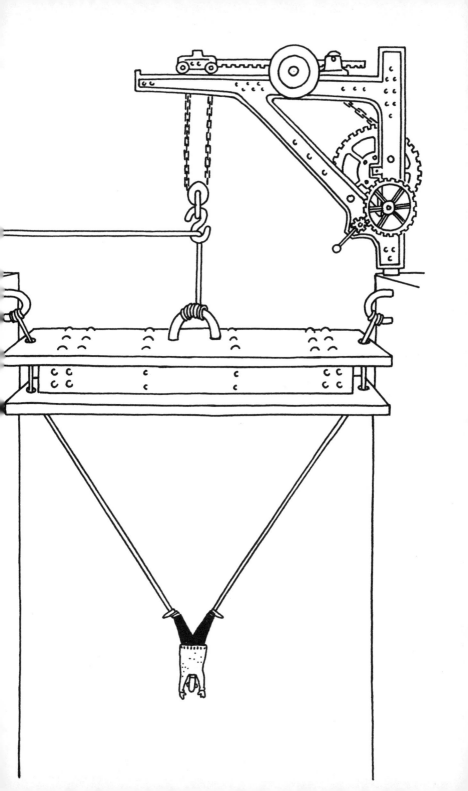

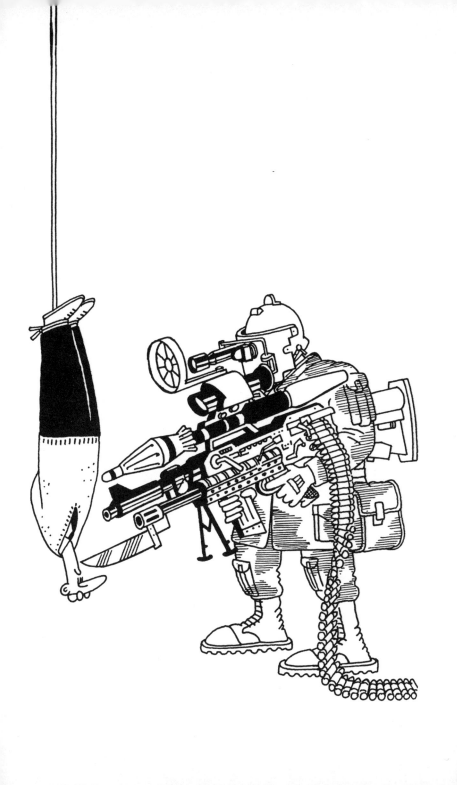

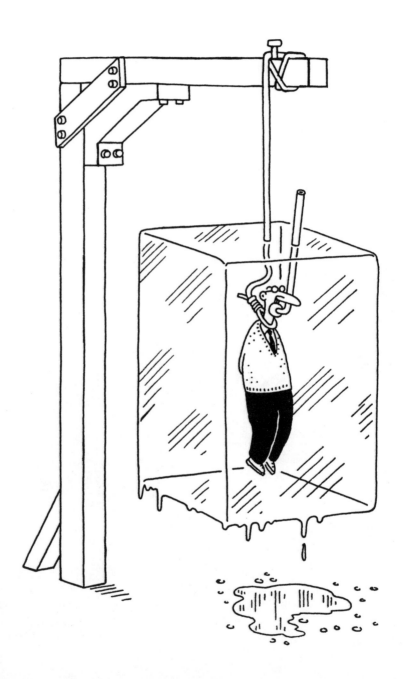

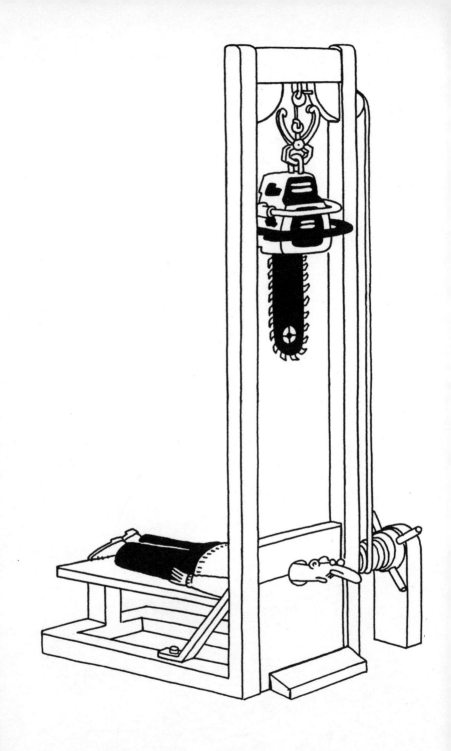

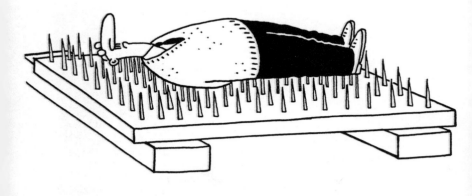

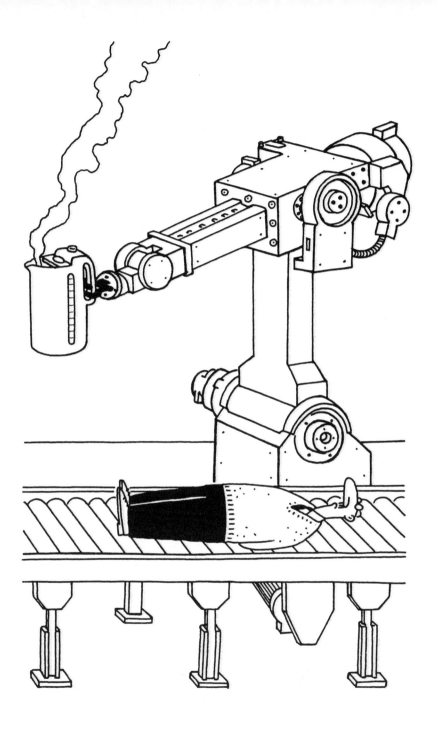

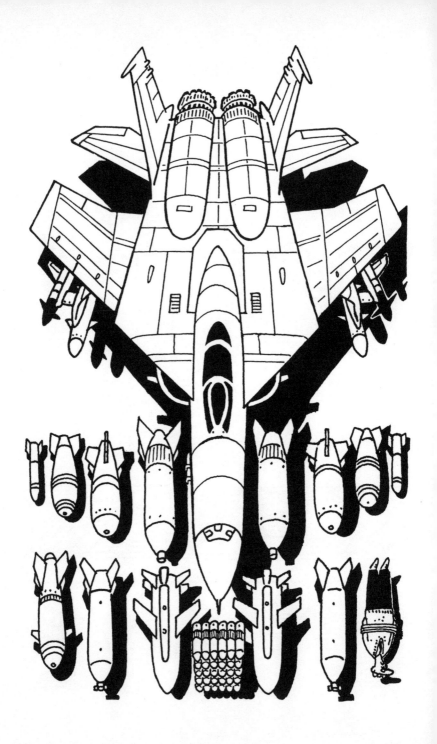

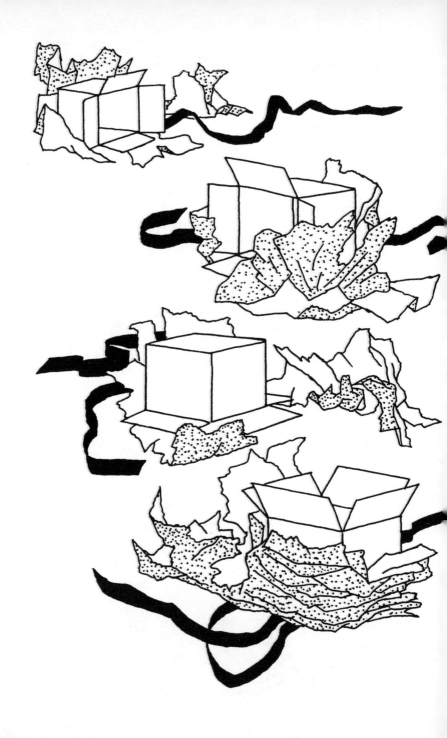

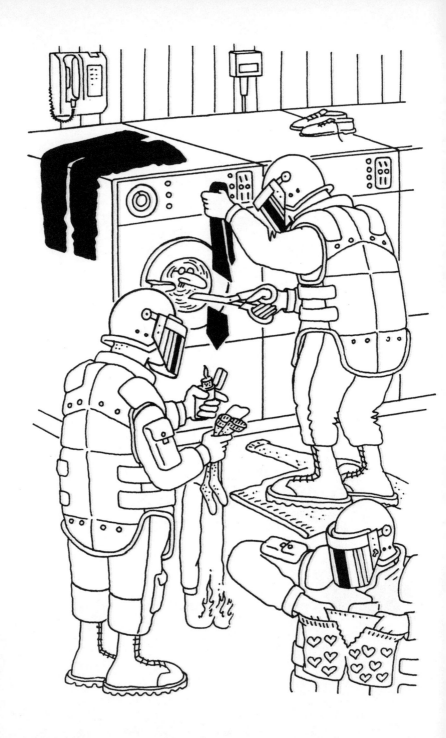

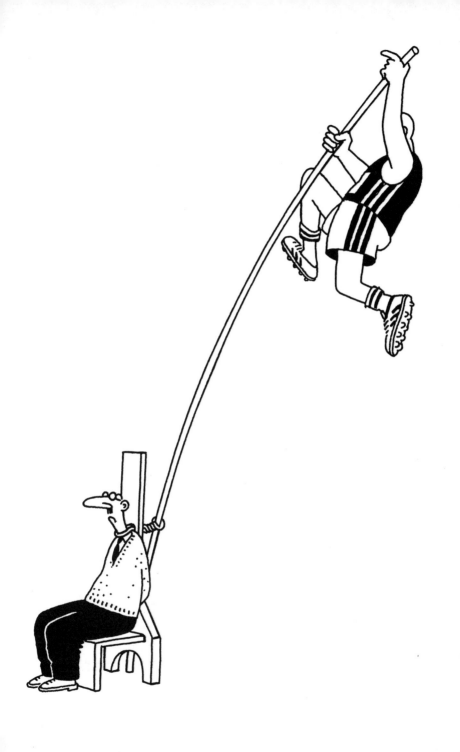

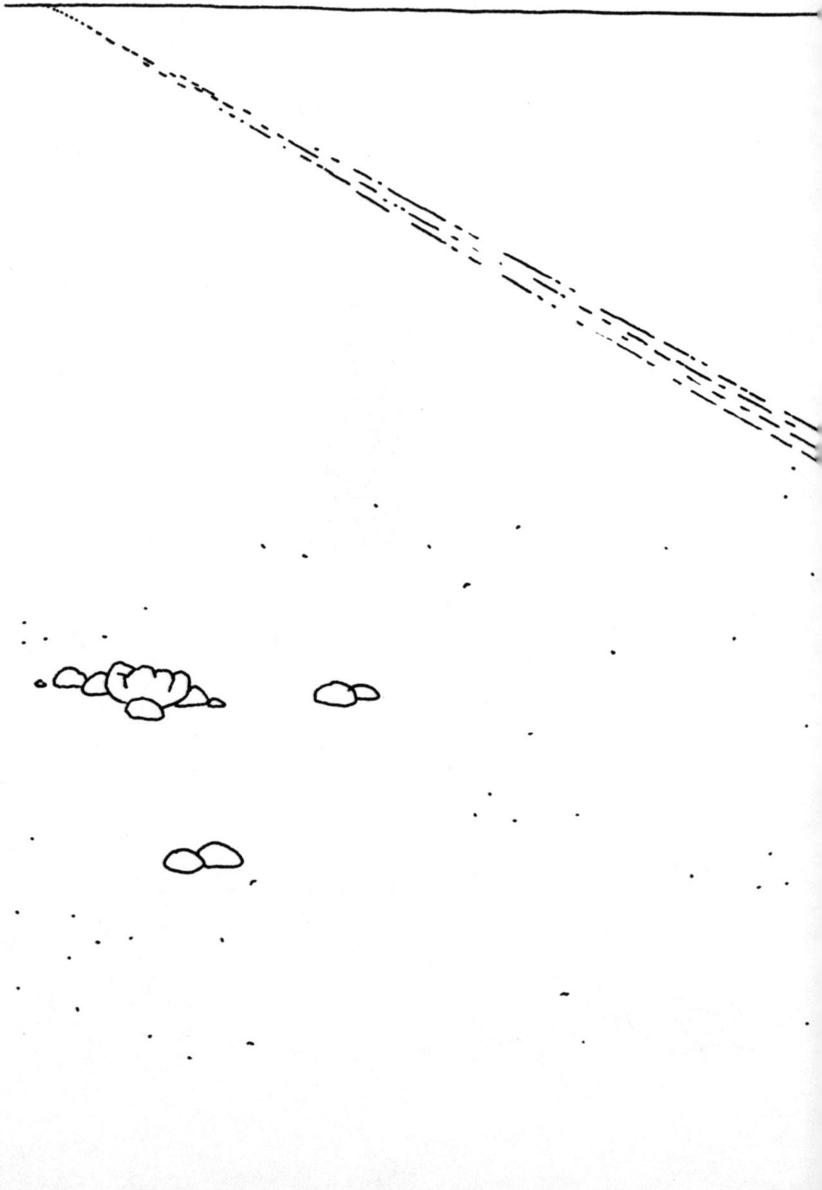

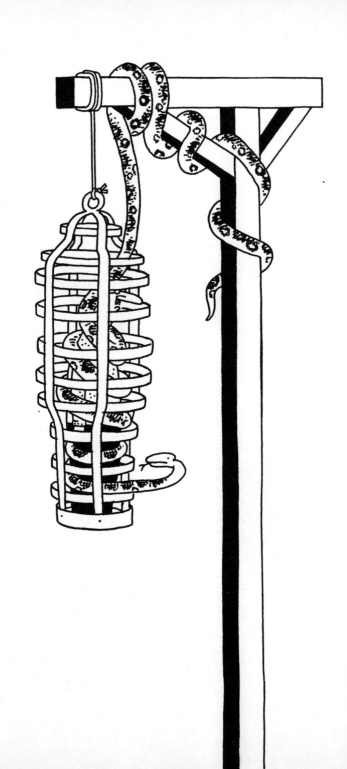

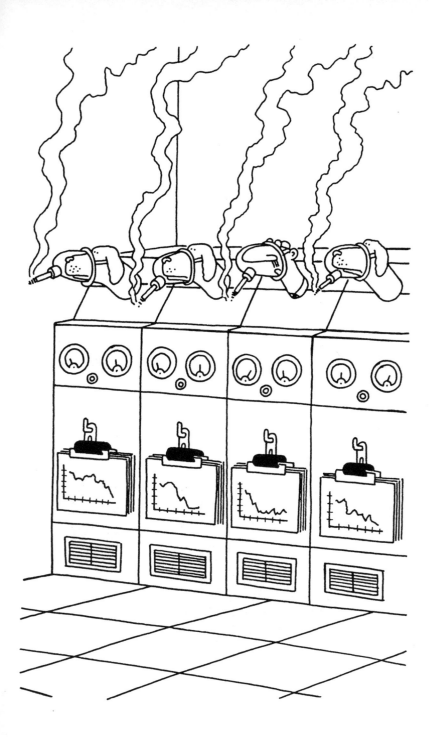

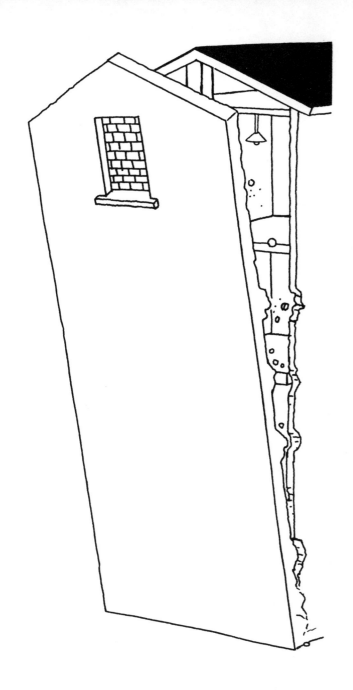

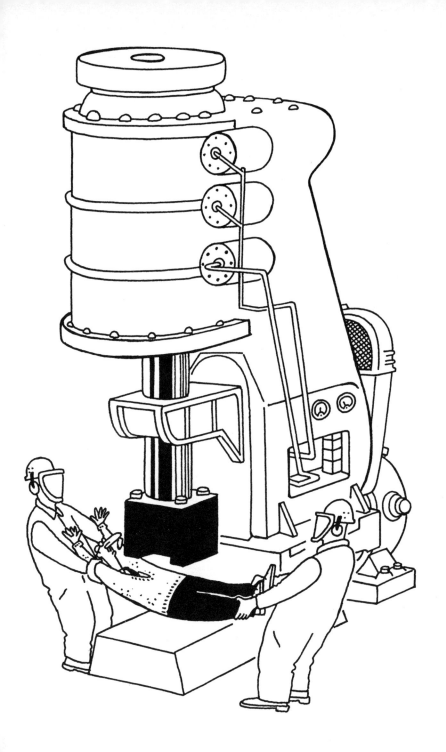

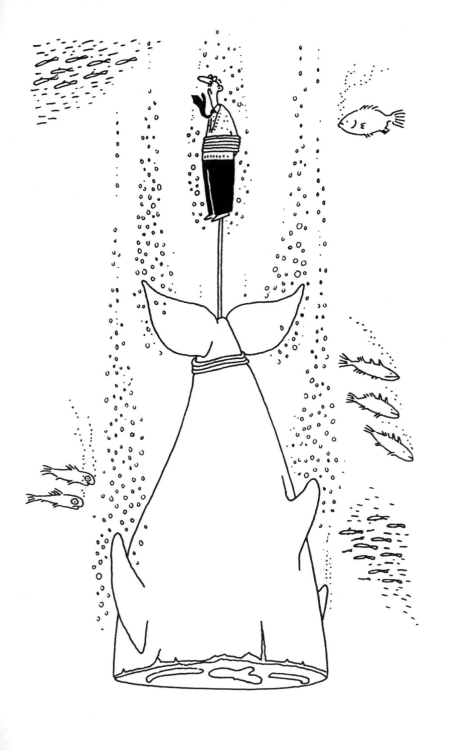

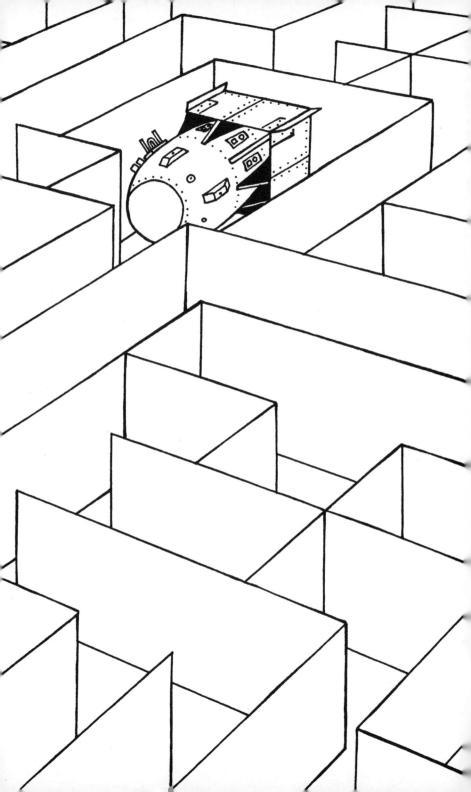

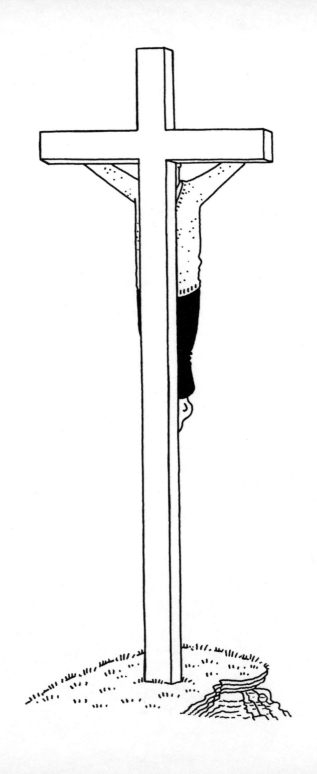

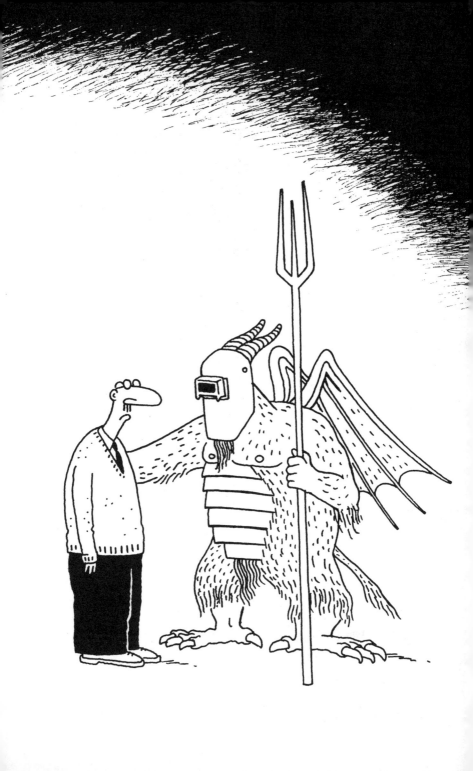

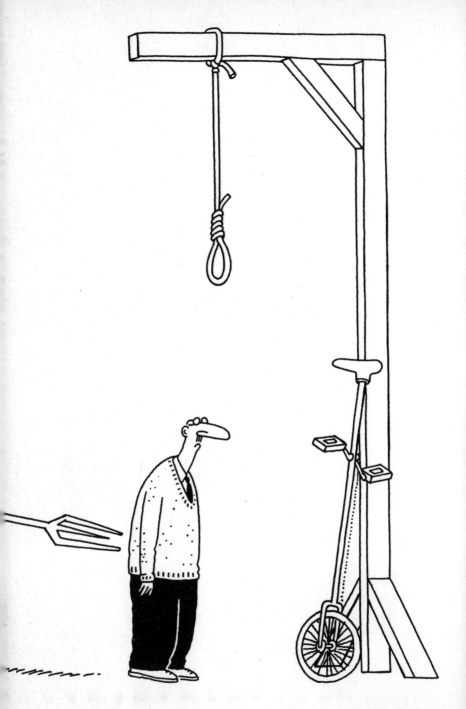

BANX 95